To Erin

CAN SUCH THINGS BE?

with love

[signatures]

ZOOOommm!!!

£50

www.LAWRENCE PRESTIDGE.com

Look out for other books by
Lawrence Prestidge
and G William.

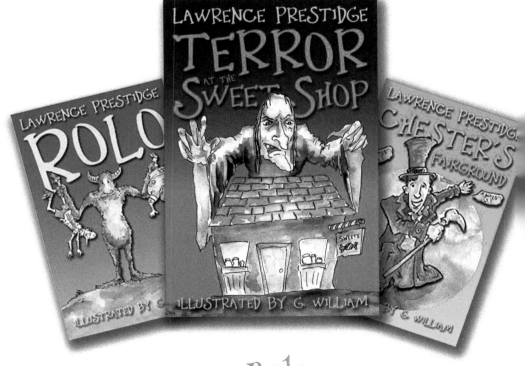

Rolo
Terror at the Sweet Shop
Chester's Fairground

CAN SUCH THINGS BE?

Lawrence Prestidge

ILLUSTRATED BY
G. WILLIAM

Matador
9 Priory Business Park,
Wistow Road, Kibworth Beauchamp,
Leicestershire. LE8 0RX
Tel: 0116 279 2299
Email: books@troubador.co.uk
Web: www.troubador.co.uk/matador
Twitter: @matadorbooks

ISBN 978 1789015 003

British Library Cataloguing in Publication Data.
A catalogue record for this book is available from the British Library.

Printed and bound by CPI Group (UK) Ltd, Croydon, CR0 4YY

Matador is an imprint of Troubador Publishing Ltd

Contents

Miles the Magpie

Miles the magpie wasn't very smart,
He tried his best to impress but he was doomed from the start.
His beak was slightly bent, his eyes were very beady,
His skinny wings were weak and those legs were just plain weedy.

Poor Miles wasn't even elegant when he flew
But Miles wasn't bothered because he loved to poo.
He would glide in the sky, beady eyes looking down,
Searching out a helpless victim lurking on the ground.

He pooed on cars - all different makes,
He pooed on children's birthday cakes.
Miles was just unstoppable- he pooed in every place.
In a cup final at Wembley he pooed in the ref's face!

One time he flew to America - he darted, dashed and sped,
He whooshed and swooshed and just in time hit the president's head!
One evening feeling very mean,

He dropped his dung upon the Queen!

But the last victim Miles
picked out he would never forget,
This would be a victim
that he would soon regret.
He chose a lowly farmer
– first name Reg.
Miles would poo across his farm–
on all his fruit and veg.

The apples and the carrots - tomatoes for his soup -
Had all felt the full force of Miles' poop.
What Miles didn't know was that Reg had hatched a plan,
Mr Reginald Greenbottom was a very clever man.

Reg started to grow berries knowing that's what magpies love
Hoping it would bring Miles down from high above.
Miles noticed the berries and soon glided down,
After he made sure no-one was around.

He started pecking away and filling up his gut,
Eating berries galore - he couldn't believe his luck,
But when he was done and it was time to fly away
He noticed that his legs were making him stay.

Miles flapped his wings as hard as he could
But still on the berry bush he stood.
Miles was stuck he didn't know what to do...
For Reg had pasted the bush with super-glue.

Reg looked out the window and smiled with rampant glee,
He needed to get to Miles before that bird broke free.
He headed up to Miles taking with him his prized cow.
Miles began to panic "WHAT DO I DO NOW?"

"DON'T SHOOT ME!" Cried Miles "OR ARE YOU LEAVING ME TO ROT?"
"Kill you!?" Replied Reg, "I should think not!"
"THEN SET ME FREE!" Yelled Miles "AND I WON'T BOTHER YOU ONE BIT!"
"Time to taste your own medicine" said Reg
                                    "let's see how you like it."

Reg's cow turned around - Miles' fate drew near.
Miles knew what was coming - his eyes filled with fear.
He tried hard to escape but still from the bush he hung...
A few seconds later - Miles was completely covered in DUNG!

Jessica the Wrestler

This is a story about a girl named Jessica,
Who wanted nothing more than to be a wrestler.
Some girls want to be a vet and look after sick cats,
But Jessica wanted to slam opponents to the mat.

Every day her eyes would be glued to the TV,
Watching her wrestling heroes with glee,
Saying to herself "one day that will be me,"
Through press-ups and vitamins it came to be.

Of course her parents did show concern,
At all the wrestling moves she would learn:
She power-slammed dolls, one after the other;
Spine-bustered the dog, before pinning her brother.

The bullies at school all ran in fear,
Anytime that Jessica was near.
She'd give those bullies a thunderous chop,
Whenever the bullies refused to stop

Stealing kid's sweets or just being mean.
Jessica would always make them scream.
A figure four leglock would do the trick,
A suplex, a powerbomb or just a drop kick.

Her parents did help her wrestling craze
Getting her lessons to support this 'phase'.
They never could guess what would unfold
When Jessica won Olympic Gold!

She beat a sumo wrestler with no trouble at all
And was soon on the podium standing tall.
Now she wrestles in countries near and far
'Cause now she's a wrestling superstar!

Her parents wanted her to be a nurse
Instead she's the:

Champion of the universe!

SUE THE BUTCHER

Sue was a butcher, twice as wide as she was tall.
Wiry was her hair, vile her smile, but that's not all...
Sue was the most disgusting woman you'll ever ever see.
But most gross of all: the meat she sold for tea.

Most butchers sell beef, chicken and delicious ham.
Most butchers sell bacon, pork and legs of lamb.
Did Sue do this? Of course not, no.
Instead she cut up children so.
What people thought was the finest lamb,
Was really Sophie, Molly and Sam!
When families thought it was sausages to eat,
It was really toes from children's feet!

Now Luke was a smart lad, top of the class and best in school,
Captain of the football team, he couldn't be more cool.
He wasn't prepared though for the horror that he'd see
When he realised he was eating his friend Ruby for his tea!
Sunk deep in his steak was the necklace of his mate,
Which now just lay there, upon his empty plate.
Luke was filled up with all kinds of emotion,
But most of all he needed a plan that he could put in motion.
His mother wouldn't listen, his father just denied,
So Luke needed proof if other children weren't to die.

He snuck out of the house late at night
And headed down to Sue's shop quickly, on his bike.
Sneaking like a ninja, or a whisper, or a breath.
He knew if Sue saw him - he'd be finished, it was death.
Luke tiptoed to a window, he felt terror at the sight,
Sue was chopping up poor children in the dead of night!
He started to run but couldn't tell a relation,
So he darted like a rocket to the nearest police station.

He shot through the door in a big sweaty heap
To see PC Andrews on his chair, fast asleep.

"WAKE UP!"

Cried Luke, "THERE'S MURDER IN THE TOWN!"
But PC Andrews slept away without a frown.
Luke had to find a way to make the trouble known,
So he picked up the police department's massive megaphone.
The noise was loud as thunder, it was pointed at his ear,
There really was no way that PC Andrews wouldn't hear.

"HELLLP!!"

Shouted Luke, PC Andrews took flight,
Leaping in the the air with his heart full of fright.

"PLEASE I NEED YOUR HELP," Luke cried once more,
After PC Andrews landed heavily on the floor.
He looked confused,
His bottom bruised,
But Luke he had no more time to lose.
"SUE'S SNATCHING KIDS AND SERVING THEM FOR LUNCH AS TASTY MEAT
BUT ONCE YOU AND THE COPS ARE THERE WE'LL SOON HAVE HER BEAT,
ALREADY THERE ARE FIFTEEN KIDS THAT HAVE BEEN TAKEN."

"WAIT!"

Cried PC Andrews, "What I had for lunch, wasn't bacon!?"
Right he bellowed, "Follow me we need to stop her plan,
Before more little kids end up swimming in the frying pan."

PC Andrews grabbed his handcuffs, quick as a flash,
And raced to Sue's vile butcher shop in a breathless dash.
Approaching the same window that gave Luke such a fright
It now was clean, calm, serene - not a drop of blood in sight.
PC Andrews turned bright red, it was clear that he was furious
Believing that the story Luke had told was quite spurious.

"Don't waste my time!" The copper screamed

But then he saw what Luke had seen...
A child's head, there on the ground!
It bounced about and rolled around.

PC Andrews had to puke,
He narrowly avoided Luke.
Carefully ignoring the sick on the floor,
PC Andrews kicked in the door.

But as he entered there Sue stood,
Her apron splattered red with blood.
"I'm arresting you for violent crimes"
PC Andrews said. Sue checked the time.

"IT SEEMS MY BUTCHERING'S STILL NOT DONE
I WON'T BE COMING" and she spun.
she swung a cleaver at the PC'S head,

If he didn't move quick he'd soon be dead.
Luke yelled out "QUICK PC DUCK"
PC Andrews kicked out a foot.
It seems that Andrews was a kung fu master,
Sue was quick but he was faster.
He kicked her square, right to the gut,

The cleaver slipped as Andrews ducked.
This led to a disgusting thing,
The cleaver in the air did spin,
It sliced and diced the butcher's neck,
It snicker-snacked, it snacker-snecked.
Blood then spluttered everywhere,
It even went in poor Luke's hair
Sue's vile head slammed to the floor.
Her lifeless body beside the door.
The evil butcher had been taken down
How would they explain this to the rest of the town?

Sue simply disappeared; not a word was said.
But they pulled down the butchers and replaced it with **veg**
Grown in allotments for the town to share
And the people came together with love and care.
They strung up beans and cared for cabbages,
They grew crunchy carrots and spicy radishes.

PC Andrews opened a dojo training kids in **Kung Fu**.
Because you never know when you'll need
A spinning kick, do you?

Gets My Goat

What if Pigs kept us in cages as we rolled around in mud?
Before everything ended with a grisly thud.

I don't think it would be very fun
If it was a Turkey stuffing your bum.

I really don't think that you would laugh
To be a Fox's trendy scarf.

I bet you would think 'What the heck!'
If you saw a lucky human's foot round a rabbit's neck.

Imagine if it was alligators that did brag
About their luxury new human bag.

Maybe we humans are just too vain
To see that all we bring animals is pain.
If someone betrays us we say 'snake,'
When it's the humans that are really fake.

Let's learn to be as loyal as a dog,
Instead of eating legs from noble frogs.

Love Thy NEIGHBOUR

If you have good neighbours then count yourself blessed,
Poor Ben had a neighbour that made him stressed.
Gwen was her name, like a sewer was her smell
And what she enjoyed was making life HELL!

You see, Ben enjoyed sport - none more than football
But he had to be cautious of the garden wall.
Whether basket or tennis or rugby or foot,
The balls that went over all ended kaput!

If a ball ever landed in evil Gwen's yard,
She would take a sharp knife and would stab it real hard.
Ben would peer o'er the wall with a tear in his eye,
As Gwen would cackle

"Die ball die!"

And then when the ball was completely flat,
She'd serve it straight up to her mangy, fat, cat.
Gwen's cat would eat anything in her house
But its favourite was 'Football souffle a la mouse'

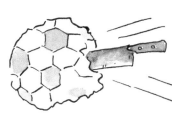

Ball after ball would disappear,
Was this the end of Ben's sporting career?
Ben finally decided that because of Gwen,
He'd never - not ever - kick a ball again.

But a friend would help with Ben's dismay.
His cunning friend Dan said "We'll make that witch pay."
They took an old basketball and made up a plan,
If this went well they'd be legends of man.

Dan put a slit in the ball and said "Lets fill her up"
"With what?" Asked Ben, "With disgusting muck."

Then over the next couple of days,
They filled that ball up in so many ways.
They cracked in some eggs
And mixed it up nice.
They added mouldy cheese
And ground up some ice.
They poured in half a bottle of
Dad's favourite gin,
They dumped in all the rubbish
From inside of the bin.
To make it much worse they put in dog poo
They rummaged around for some vomit too.

Now you cannot imagine the stench this created,
The longer it sat and the longer they waited
The more it fermented and festered and grew
Till the gloop and the gunk in the ball turned to goo.
A nuclear basketball oozing with toxic waste
It was time for the boys to make haste.

Now there was no going back on this plan,
Ben smiled and he nodded,
'It's time' whispered Dan.
Dan was the look-out,
Ben hopped over the wall
He muttered,
"Quick Dan - pass me over the ball."
Dan lobbed him the ball,
But that is just when
Everything got very scary for Ben...

There she stood like a ghost in a graveyard,
Gwen's piercing eyes glared and Ben swallowed real hard.
She opened her mouth "I DON'T THINK SO." Gwen grunted
"THAT BALL'S IN MY GARDEN, THAT'S MINE THAT YOU'VE
PUNTED"
"Run Ben" yelled out Dan "Come on, run real quick"
Gwen laughed "I HOPE IT WAS WELL WORTH THE KICK!"
Ben quickly hopped back over his garden wall,
Of course as he hopped he was leaving the ball.

Gwen reached in her apron and pulled out a knife
Yelling "IT'S TIME TO END THIS BALL'S SORRY LIFE!"
She raised the knife high, and cackled out loud
And knife met the ball with a shocking

KERPOW!!!!

What happened next's too distressing to tell,
But never have you smelt such a disgusting smell.
I don't want to talk about it,
don't want to dwell,
But the stench was enough;
you will recognise well:
It was baby sick, doggy poo,
deep fried banana
Mouldy beans, warm ice cream,
fluff from a llama.
Evil young brothers with jars full of toenails,
Bogey pies baked for your tea packed with snails
It was gross and disgusting,
vomit inducing
It made eyes weep, sheep bleat, killed sleep
And left you in tears,
And Gwen had to think of that smell, for **10** solid years.

But the plan worked -
For if ever a ball landed near Gwen's shack,
In a matter of seconds she'd throw it straight back.

P17

Jake and Jack

Jake and Jack were two friends at school,
But it was always Jack that was left looking the fool.
For Jake would always dare Jack to do stupid things,
Jake knew just what to say to pull Jack's strings.

Jake would always give Jack a stupid dare,
Like turning up to school in his underwear.
Whilst Jake would roll around and laugh
Poor Jack would feel the teacher's wrath!

Jake was jumping up and down with glee
When he convinced him - on the headteacher's car to wee.
Jake told Jack there would be no harm,
In setting off the school fire alarm.

Jack accepted detention, after detention
Just so he could have Jake's attention.
Jack watched Jake laugh in the sun
Whilst sat in detention deprived of his fun.

Then Jack decided the day had come,
For him to stop being so dumb.
From then on we would see a new Jack
Determined to get his own back.

The next time Jake had a gag,
Jack said, "Okay but hold onto my bag."
And as Jack walked away
from the school cafe

There was a loud boom,
And custard filled the entire room!
Jack's cunning plan, all along,
Was to make a simple custard bomb.

And as for his friend poor old Jake,
He looked in a messy, 'custardy' state.
But for clever old Jack - the thing that was best
Was when the teacher screamed,

"JAKE CLEAN UP THIS MESS!"

THE
F O X
and the
WOLF

Once upon a time there was a wolf who loved to eat.
He'd scoff up anything, raw or sour or sweet.
It got to the stage where he put on so much weight
He looked like a hairy bowling ball, filling up his plate.

Of course he went to a slimming class - insisted by his friend
But this was a disaster with a gruesome end.
One day the slimming instructor was running slightly late
Wolf couldn't wait for snack time, so he gobbled up his mate!

One day the wolf was napping
After a hefty lunch,
When he was suddenly awoken
By a punch-punch-punch.
It was the cunning fox,
He danced and laughed
The wolf growled
That fox would feel his wrath.
The wolf, he hated foxes -
They weren't something he could eat
This one was cunning and difficult to beat.
He loved to torment the wolf, loved to play tricks,
Like one time he pretended that Twiglets were sticks,
The fox ate up all the snacks leaving him none.
Another time he told the wolf that stones were buns.
The wolf cracked his teeth and had sores on his tongue.
Stealing food from the wolf was the fox's idea of fun.
Yet here stood the fox at the wolf's front door,
He wouldn't let him in like he had done before!

The wolf yelled in ANGER!! his voice full of annoyance,

Whilst the fox danced inside with flair and flamboyance.

"You're just so easy to enrage," joked the laughing fox
The wolf just clenched his fists and, swinging hard, began to box.
But the cunning beast just grinned, not caring in the slightest,
"You might be big," mocked the fox,
                    "but your belly's not the lightest."

Fox danced behind the sofa, fox danced across the chairs,
That podgy wolf grew tired and soon sat panting on the stairs.
"Being cunning's just what foxes do,
Thinking's too tough for a wolf like you.
I suppose that's why they call it outfoxed,
You need to learn to think outside the box.
I know that you're angry- but you shouldn't be hasty
I only came to tell you that I saw some fine pastry."

The wolf held back his anger and started sniffing,
His nose said that somewhere a meat pie was whiffing.
The vicar's wife had left the meat pie right by the window
Ignoring the fox; wolf approached the vicarage slow.
Just inches from the delicious meat pie,
The fox reappeared and caught his eye.
"Quick get down" said the fox with a mutter.
"The vicar's wife is coming and she's got a meat cutter!"

Ducking down quickly below the open window,
The grin on the fox's face began to grow.
The cunning fox jumped up, ate the pie in one bite,
He looked back at the wolf who was ready to fight.

"Ah...outfoxed again" said the fox with a nervous grin
"You're finished!" said the wolf "I'll tear you limb from limb"

"Wait!" Cried the fox with a desperate yell
"You need to listen first- there's a secret to tell."
The wolf listened "This better be good... or you're for the chop"
"Wolfie my friend- let's raid the butcher's shop...
I'll distract the butcher whilst you eat all of the meat
It'll be your own buffet- all you can eat!"

That's why I couldn't let you eat that pie!
Your stomach needs room Wolfie-
I'm not the bad guy!"

The wolf's anger once again went away
"All you can eat butchers?!

HOORAY, HOORAY!"

The wolf dashed to the butchers, carrying the fox
But he dropped him off by a nearby phone box.
Fox said:
"I'll distract the butcher by giving him a ring
Whilst you have a meat banquet fit for a king."

The fox rang the shop,
The butcher went to the back.
The wolf ran inside,
It was now time to snack…

Sausages and HAM
kidneys and liver
The sight of the meat
Set the wolf in a quiver.

He grabbed mouthfuls of **BACON**

And gobfuls of **TONGuE**

He munched on some **tripe**

And he gorged on some **LUNG**

He gobbled and munched and filled himself up,
Then he sat down full-bellied in the middle on the shop.

But meanwhile that fox he was using the phone,
To tell the poor butcher that a wolf was in his home!
Straight to the shop the butcher did run
But not before he nipped to the shed for his gun.

Now that fox was quite boastful and incredibly proud
So he couldn't resist seeing his plan going down.
He snuck to the window and peered through the door
And spotted the bloated wolf sat on the floor.

The butcher appeared in the door with his gun,
He tripped over the fox and the wolf began to run
It's hard to move fast when your belly's full of meat
But the power of fear awoke the wolf's feet.

P24

The fox heard a **Gun-Shot!!!**
Straight through his HEART,
As a piece of his plan, this wasn't part!

The butcher's shop now displays a fox's head.

The wolf? Oh don't worry the wolf is not dead.
The wolf learned his lesson and he's no longer greedy,
He's lost all that weight and is incredibly

SPEEDY

To Play or Not to Play?

Jed, George, Sam and Tom were four friends from school,
With their jokes and their pranks they were likeable fools.
In Drama the routine was always the same,
For Drama to them was just a big game.
They could act like a robot, or mimic a tree,
But if work was to be done they would just turn and flee.

If, for a second Miss turned from the class
The boys would be off out the door in a flash.
They'd hide in the stock cupboard surrounded by plays,
With Pinter and Miller they'd waste out their days.
Surrounded by scripts that just sat there unread,
The boys all sat there; quite quiet, playing dead.

Till one day while hiding they grew really bored
And Sam began to look at the books that were stored.
A play called Macbeth looked somewhat appealing
Though the cover was dusty and broken and peeling.
Handwritten and ancient the cover did creak,
When opened a ghost appeared and tried to speak.

It was balding and beardy and it spoke in a mutter,
It had a good cough and it had a good splutter.
A ghost with a cough to them seemed quite odd
But I suppose being stuck in a book is a dusty job.
"To be free at last!" The ghost did proclaim
To which Jed replied "wait..isn't that..what's his name?"

"My name!?" The ghost said, his shock was quite clear,
"My dear boy- I am the great William Shakespeare."
"Oh, Shakespeare... that guy who's so boring."
"Oh that guy" said Tom "His plays have me snoring..."
Shakespeare's face was in horror at what the boys said,
He was used to high praise and he had a big head.

"My plays they are legend" snarked Shakespeare at once
"It is clear to me that you are a cloth-headed dunce,
Romeo and Juliet, Hamlet, Macbeth,
How dare you insinuate they bore you to death
My plays have crowds lining up at the doors"
To which George replied "I much prefer Star Wars..."

"Alas my young fool
I cannot debate,
I have wishes to hand
Out before it's too late."
"What do you mean?"
Sam asked "are you like a genie?"
"A genius genie I am: yes indeedy.
I have wishes to grant for you four,
But you'd better move quick
I'm beginning to bore."

"Wishes! For me?" Jed asked the ghost with glee.
"Yes indeed and once done, then I'll be set free"
Sam cried "I know exactly what wish I'd pick!"

"Good" replied Shakespeare. "lets do this quick"
"Okay, well this wish might seem quite weird...
But what I want is a really, I mean really, cool beard."

Sam made his wish clear and then with a snap
His wish was granted... just like that.
However, it was not what Sam had in mind...
As the ghost of Shakespeare was feeling far from kind.
Sam's beard was as white as snow and grew very, very long,
His wish had clearly gone horribly wrong!

Sam was actually the youngest of the four,
But he now had a hideous beard dragging on the floor!
"I take it back!" Cried Sam. His beard looked horrific,
"I'm sorry," chuckled Shakespeare "You need to be more specific."
"Okay my go!" Cried out Tom,
Who knew his wish all along.

"I'm going to be the envy of every kid in all the towns,
Because what I want on me is a million pounds."
And then with a snap...
Tom's wish was granted just like that...
Well not exactly like that..
Tom did have a million pounds... of body fat
Tom now was the fattest person alive,
He looked like he had eaten a house...or five.

Tom cried and he sobbed "I meant a million pounds of money!"
Shakespeare replied "Ah, but this is far more funny."

"Okay my go." said Jed who'd been thinking hard,
He wanted to make sure he wasn't caught off guard.
"What I've always wanted is to soar real high,
So my wish to you is simply to fly!"
And then with a snap,
Jed's wish was granted like that,
The magic from Shakespeare began to flow,
As Jed transformed into a small black crow.

Shakespeare continued to laugh... "haha now that was fun"

He turned his attention to George and said "And then there was one
One wish left, get on it with, for I long to be free
And see what this little old world thinks of me."
That gave George an idea, as the brains of the group,
If he could pull this off it would be a massive coup*
"Oh I don't know.. a wish? I simply can't pick
Shakespeare grew frustrated, "Just say one quick!"

George cleared his throat and yelled loud and clear:

"I WISH THERE WAS NEVER SUCH A PERSON AS WILLIAM SHAKESPEARE!"

And then with a snap
George's wish was granted just like that.
Now William realised what he had done,
The panic set in and he tried to run,
The Ghost of the bard began to disappear,
As clever George stood with a grin: ear to ear.
Unfortunately for the others they had to stay the same...
And suddenly they couldn't remember the ghost's name
For all knowledge of Shakespeare slipped from their heads,
While they remembered the wishes they should never have said,
But it wasn't all doom and gloom - there were positives ahead...
Because in history there was no Shakespeare,

They learnt about Dinosaurs instead!

* Technically this is pronounced Coo but that's artistic licence for you

P30

THE BALLAD OF LARRY

Now Larry was just the quiet type,
He went to work; lived with his wife.
They didn't have much when it came to cash
But they never wanted anything flash.

Then one day a man came up to his door,
He was tall with no neck, he'd not seen him before.
"I'm Brian Damage, you might know my name
Helping people like you, is part of my game."

Larry looked confused, he didn't need any help...
He had a happy wife and he had his health.
"Nah!" said Brian, in a voice like sandpaper
"Just listen we'll do this sooner not later."

"A loan shark like me just lends you some cash,
You spend it on what you like, no questions asked,
Then all you gotta do is pay it all back...with interest
You can use it to invest, if that's yer thing."

"With what?" squeaked Larry, feeling slightly worried,
This chap Brian Damage seemed like a big bully.
"Wiv intrest" said Brian and he pulled out some cash,
Stuffed it in Larry's hands and left in a dash.

So Larry forgot all about his previous self,
And began to admire his new found wealth.
Till Brian shouted back "Oh, one more fing, if I don't get paid
You're getting flayed, a rug from your skin, is getting made."

Larry just smiled and waved Brian goodbye,
He was already thinking of the things he would buy.

But when she got home his wife wasn't pleased,
Larry had taken his newly found cash
And with it decided to make a big splash!

He spent his new money on clothes and cars,
Insisted they ate in restaurants and bars,
One time while he was feeling particularly dumb
He brought a baby elephant for his poor, confused mum.

He got even sillier with money when drunk,
After a bottle of wine,
He went online,
And bought a cut out...of

Donald Trump!

But all of his spending he soon would regret,
As he sank ever deeper and deeper in debt.

His wife was annoyed by his spendthrift ways,
She missed the old Larry and their happier days.

Larry became such a **pompous buffoon**,
His wife couldn't help but to leave him soon.

But then Brian arrived and demanded he be paid,
One million pounds or Larry's flesh would be flayed.
When Larry complained and said "I need more time"
Brian just laughed and said "That skin will be mine!"

Larry felt sick, this would change his life,

He enjoyed being **RICH**, it was certainly nice
To spend all that cash on those pointless things
But he was slightly more worried by the loss of his skin!

Larry needed cash and he needed it now,
He needed more money but he didn't know how
So he gambled on horses, invested and bailed.

He tried starting a business that sold **RACING SNAILS.**

But nothing made money, in fact he lost more,
And in only a day Brian would be at his door.
He went to the park, he was hoping and praying
When upon the grass he saw something laying.

Just as he was kissing his skin goodbye,
He saw on the grass, a rare butterfly.
Larry knew this butterfly was very rare
To catch it would make him a millionaire.

This butterfly was beautiful and one of a kind,
Larry could only see cash signs in his mind.
He began to sneak up as it sat in the sun
But it fluttered away: QUICK LARRY RUN!

Larry chased it past the shops and bars
   He chased it on the road-
  He had to dodge cars -
He chased down a snicket
    And ran up a lane,
      He kept right on running,
        Though his legs were in pain.
   Larry chased that rare butterfly
Into the night,
    He needed to have it
        Before it was light.
      At one point it landed on a sleeping dog's nose,
Larry saw it reclining and suddenly FROZE.
He couldn't afford to scare it away
And he knew if he woke the dog he'd soon pay.

He crept slowly...
Carefully...
Tried to be quiet.

If that dog awoke there'd be more than a r i o t.
Larry cautiously cupped the prize in his hand,
He'd soon be one of the richest in the land.
He'd pay off Brian and his skin would be free
He couldn't stay calm and he screamed out

"WOoooopeeeee!"

Larry was delighted, he was jumping and leaping.
But he forgot never to wake a dog when it's sleeping...
Larry's joy soon turned to alarm
When he felt a huge slobbery bite on his arm.

The dog bit him hard and Larry hated to see
That because of the pain the butterfly was now free...
The chase began again, "Come back" he would beg
Larry ran after it fast, with a dog on his leg.
It was harder to chase the thing in the dark,
But Larry followed that butterfly into the park.
The butterfly landed but left Larry mad
As it settled in the pond on a green lily-pad.
Larry slowly entered, prepared to get soggy
At least now the dog was detached from his body.

He focused on that butterfly, precious as gold
Determined to get it - even though he was freezing cold.
But just as he reached out to grab for his goal...
Up leapt a frog and swallowed it whole.
Larry couldn't believe it.. he yelled.

He broke down in the pond and began to cry.

"WHY FROG WHY?!"

Now when you see Larry... he's a real unique specimen
Because Larry is the only man alive who's pure SKELETON.
His wife is quite happy now Larry has gone
She lives in a nursing home with her old mum.
But if there is a message to never forget...
Remember poor Larry and:

NEVER GET IN DEBT!

Nan and Grandpa

You may not think that I remember all the things you've done;
From Sunday dinners, veg galore, to endless cold school runs.
From your very first hello, to all the lengths you'd go,
For letting me choose the channel to watch my favourite show.
For forgiving me when I was bad.
For making me smile when I felt sad.
For pushing me on the swing,
For all the birthday gifts you'd bring.
For all the chocolate in your handbag
I want to thank you Nan and Grandad.
No matter how much I'm grown,
I'll know I'm not alone.
So I write this poem as a gift to brighten up your day
And I will never forget the love you show, in so many ways.

GWilliam's Sketchbook